Diplodocus
The dippy idea

Written by Fran Bromage
Illustrated by Richard Watson

MiLes KeLLy

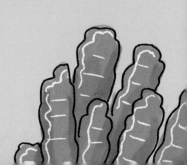

There was once a **huge and hungry** Diplodocus called Dora.

Dora often had lots of **dippy ideas** and was easily confused.

'Hmm... my favourite leaves are on that side of the tree,' she thought, one day.

'So I'll stand here and **twist my neck** like this to reach them!'

"Dora! You nearly **stepped on me!**" shouted a small Ornitholestes. "Head over there will you?"

"But my head IS over there," Dora replied, confused.

But before Dora could move away, an old Diplodocus appeared.

"Sssh! There's an Allosaurus about!" he hissed.

She watched as the herd swung their **enormous necks** and tails at the Allosaurus to scare them off.

After the fight **everyone was hungry**, but they also wanted to think of new ways to **scare off** the Allosaurus.

The Diplodocus were tired of all the **neck-swinging** and having their meals interrupted.

"We could **disguise** ourselves... as trees," suggested Dora, "with leaves on our heads!"

But no one took Dora seriously, so she **wandered off** on her own.

Deeper in the forest, Dora spotted a Stegosaurus frightening off another Allosaurus.

"You did it!" said Dora, strolling over to the smiling Stegosaurus called Peggy.

"I wish I had amazing armoured plates on my back," Dora sighed.

Peggy offered to help Dora make her own armour with mud and palm leaves.

"This is a great idea!" smiled Dora. "We'll all look so fierce – no Allosaurus will dare to come near us!"

But **everyone laughed** at Dora's idea and went back to eating leaves.

Poor Dora **felt sad** as she wandered down to the rocky shore to wash off her disguise.

"Never mind," said Peggy. "You'll think of something else."

"Er, Peggy?" whispered Dora. "What's that in the water?"

Dora plunged her head into the water and looked about.

"Who's in here?" she tried to say underwater (but it came out a little like 'blooob-bo-ber?')

"Try it and see," said Pete.

So Dora found some reeds. 'These will help me breathe!' she thought, and she **dived right in!**

'What a good way to hide,' thought Dora. 'We could all fit down here.'

"And there's food!" said Dora, trying a big clump of seaweed.

She didn't see the Allosaurus had returned. And she didn't see Peggy trying to warn her.

"Peggy! I've got the best idea," said Dora. "I think we should... wooooaaah!"

As Dora staggered out of the sea, she fell into a huge **puddle of mud**.

She was covered in thick, drippy black slime. The reeds, leaves and seaweed stuck out at all angles.

The Allosaurus had never seen anything so terrifying in all their lives!

"Well done Dora!" said another Diplodocus. "Your **dippy idea** wasn't so silly after all!"